Note to parents

Little Owl Christmas Books present Christmas classics in an enjoyable and popular format. The beautifully illustrated pages offer plenty for children to talk about and can be used as a starting point for stimulating and instructive discussions with your child about Christmas and the season in general. The popular titles chosen mean that these books will be an instant success with your child who will want to read and enjoy them again and again.

Christmas Carols

Illustrated by
Ray Mutimer

Copyright © 1989 World International Publishing Limited.
All rights reserved. Published in Great Britain
by World International Publishing Limited,
An Egmont Company, Egmont House,
P.O. Box 111, Great Ducie Street, Manchester M60 3BL.
Printed in DDR.
ISBN 0 7235 1646 4

A CIP catalogue record of this book is available from the British Library

DING DONG!
MERRILY ON HIGH

Ding dong! merrily on high
In heaven the bells are ringing:
Ding dong! verily the sky
Is riven with angels singing:

CHORUS

Gloria, Hosanna in excelsis!

E'en so here below, below,
Let steeple bells be swungen,
And i-o, i-o, i-o,
By priest and people sungen:

Pray you, dutifully prime
Your matin chime, ye ringers;
May you beautifully rhyme
Your eve-time song, ye singers:

SEE AMID THE WINTER'S SNOW

See amid the winter's snow,
Born for us on earth below,
See, the tender Lamb appears,
Promised from eternal years.

CHORUS

Hail, thou ever blessed morn.
Hail, redemption's happy dawn.
Sing through all Jerusalem,
Christ is born in Bethlehem.

Lo, within a manger lies
He who built the starry skies;
He, who throned in height sublime,
Sits amid the cherubim.

Say, ye holy shepherds, say,
What your joyful news today;
Wherefore have ye left your sheep,
On the lonely mountain steep?

"As we watched at dead of night,
Lo, we saw a wondrous light;
Angels singing peace on earth,
Told us of the Saviour's birth."

Sacred Infant, all divine,
What a tender love was Thine;
Thus to come from highest bliss
Down to such a world as this.

WHILE SHEPHERDS WATCHED

While shepherds watched
  their flocks by night,
All seated on the ground,
The Angel of the Lord came down,
And glory shone around.

"Fear not," said he;
    for mighty dread
Had seized their troubled mind;
"Glad tidings of great joy I bring
To you and all mankind."

"To you in David's town this day
Is born of David's line
A Saviour, who is Christ the Lord;
And this shall be the sign:"

"The heavenly Babe
    you there shall find
To human view displayed,
All meanly wrapped
    in swathing bands,
And in a manger laid."

AWAY IN A MANGER

Away in a manger,
  no crib for a bed,
The little Lord Jesus
  laid down His sweet head.
The stars in the bright sky
  looked down where He lay,
The little Lord Jesus
  asleep on the hay.

The cattle are lowing,
  the Baby awakes,
But little Lord Jesus
  no crying He makes.
I love Thee, Lord Jesus,
  look down from the sky,
And stay by my side
  until morning is nigh.

Be near me, Lord Jesus,
  I ask Thee to stay
Close by me for ever,
  and love me, I pray:
Bless all the dear children
  in Thy tender care,
And fit us for heaven,
  to live with Thee there.

O LITTLE TOWN OF BETHLEHEM

O little town of Bethlehem,
How still we see thee lie;
Above thy deep and dreamless sleep
The silent stars go by.
Yet in thy dark streets shineth
The everlasting light;
The hopes and fears of all the years
Are met in thee tonight.

How silently, how silently
The wondrous gift is giv'n.
So God imparts to human hearts
The blessing of His heav'n.
No ear may hear His coming;
But in this world of sin,
Where meek souls will
    receive Him, still
The dear Christ enters in.

O holy Child of Bethlehem
Descend to us, we pray;
Cast out our sin, and enter in,
Be born in us today.
We hear the Christmas angels
The great glad tidings tell.
O come to us, abide with us,
Our Lord Immanuel.

O COME,
ALL YE FAITHFUL

O come, all ye faithful,
Joyful and triumphant,
O come ye, o come ye
    to Bethlehem;
Come and behold Him;
Born the King of angels;

CHORUS

O come, let us adore Him,
O come, let us adore Him,
O come, let us adore Him,
    Christ the Lord.

God of God,
Light of light,
Lo, He abhors not
   the Virgin's womb;
Very God
Begotten not created;

Sing, choirs of angels,
Sing in exultation,
Sing, all ye citizens of
   heaven above,
"Glory to God
In the highest."

Yea, Lord, we greet Thee,
Born this happy morning;
Jesu, to Thee be glory given;
Word of the Father,
Now in flesh appearing;

SILENT NIGHT

Silent night, holy night,
All is calm, all is bright.
'Round yon Virgin
    Mother and Child,
Holy Infant so tender and mild,
Sleep in heavenly peace,
Sleep in heavenly peace.

Silent night, holy night,
Shepherds quake at the sight.
Glories stream from heaven afar,
Heavenly hosts sing, "Alleluia,
Christ the Saviour is born,
Christ the Saviour is born."

Silent night, holy night,
Son of God, love's pure light,
Radiant beams from Thy holy face,
With the dawn of redeeming grace,
Jesus, Lord at Thy birth,
Jesus, Lord at Thy birth.

GOD REST YE MERRY GENTLEMEN

God rest ye merry gentlemen,
Let nothing you dismay,
For Jesus Christ, our Saviour,
Was born upon this day:
To save us all from Satan's power,
When we had gone astray:

CHORUS

O tidings of comfort and joy,
Comfort and joy,
O tidings of comfort and joy.

From God, our heavenly Father
A blessed angel came,
And unto certain shepherds
Brought tidings of the same:
How that in Bethlehem was born
The Son of God by name:

The shepherds at these tidings
Rejoiced much in mind,
And left their flocks a-feeding
In tempest, storm and wind,
And went to Bethlehem
   straightaway,
The blessed Babe to find:

HARK, THE HERALD-ANGELS SING

Hark, the herald-angels sing,
"Glory to the new-born King;
Peace on earth, and mercy mild,
God and sinners reconciled!"
Joyful, all ye nations, rise,
Join the triumph of the skies,
With the angelic host proclaim,
"Christ is born in Bethlehem."

CHORUS

Hark, the herald-angels sing,
"Glory to the new-born King."

Christ, by highest heaven adored,
Christ, the everlasting Lord,
Late in time behold Him come,
Offspring of a Virgin's womb.
Veiled in flesh the Godhead see;
Hail, the incarnate Deity,
Pleased as man with man to dwell,
Jesus, our Immanuel!

Hail, the heaven-born
    Prince of peace!
Hail, the Sun of righteousness!
Light and life to all He brings,
Risen with healing in His wings.
Mild He lays His glory by,
Born that man no more may die,
Born to raise the sons of earth,
Born to give them second birth:

IN THE BLEAK MID-WINTER

In the bleak mid-winter
Frosty wind made moan,
Earth stood hard as iron,
Water like a stone;
Snow had fallen, snow on snow,
Snow on snow,
In the bleak mid-winter
Long ago.

Our God, heav'n cannot hold Him
Nor earth sustain;
Heav'n and earth shall flee away
When He comes to reign:
In the bleak mid-winter
A stable-place sufficed
The Lord God Almighty,
Jesus Christ.

Enough for Him, whom cherubim
Worship night and day,
A breastful of milk,
And a mangerful of hay;
Enough for Him, whom angels
Fall down before,
The ox and ass and camel
Which adore.

What can I give Him
Poor as I am?
If I were a shepherd
I would bring a lamb;
If I were a wise man
I would do my part;
Yet what can I give Him –
Give my heart.

ONCE IN ROYAL DAVID'S CITY

Once in royal David's city
Stood a lowly cattle shed,
Where a mother laid her baby
In a manger for His bed:
Mary was that mother mild,
Jesus Christ her little Child.

He came down to earth
    from heaven
Who is God and Lord of all,
And His shelter was a stable,
And His cradle was a stall;
With the poor and mean and lowly
Lived on earth our Saviour holy.

And our eyes at last shall see Him,
Through His own redeeming love,
For that child so dear and gentle
Is our Lord in heaven above;
And He leads His children on
To the place where He is gone.

Not in that poor lowly stable,
With the oxen standing by,
We shall see Him; but in heaven,
Set at God's right hand on high;
Where like stars
    His children crowned
All in white shall wait around.

THE FIRST NOËL

The first Noël the angel did say
Was to certain poor shepherds
    in fields as they lay;
In fields where they lay
    keeping their sheep,
On a cold winter's night
    that was so deep.

CHORUS

Noël, Noël, Noël, Noël,
Born is the King of Israel.

They looked up and saw a star,
Shining in the east,
  beyond them far,
And to the earth
  it gave great light,
And so it continued
  both day and night.

This star drew nigh
  to the north-west,
Over Bethlehem it took its rest,
And there it did
  both stop and stay,
Right over the place
  where Jesus lay.

Then entered in those
  wise men three,
Full reverently upon their knee,
And offered there in His presence,
Their gold and myrrh
  and frankincense.